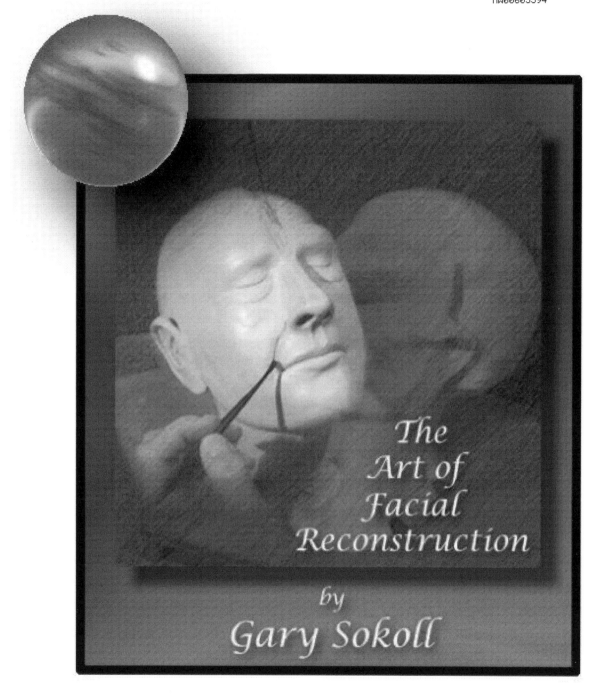

The Art of Facial Reconstruction

by

Gary Sokoll

Gary Sokoll, M.Ed., J.D.

Second Edition

The Art of
Facial Reconstruction
Second Edition

Gary Sokoll, M.Ed., J.D.

Content Written & Owned by:

PRETTY GOOD PUBLISHING

Published by:

Funeral Service Education Resource Center

FSERC

Dedicated to the Advancement of Funeral Service Education

Funeral Service Education Resource Center
12316-A North May Avenue, Suite #209
Oklahoma City, OK 73120

2nd Edition Reprinted 2016
Printed in the U.S.A.

ISBN: 978-0-9979261-0-1

Published by:
Funeral Service Education Resource Center
12316-A North May Avenue, Suite #209
Oklahoma City, Oklahoma 73120
Phone: 405-226-3155
Email: fnrleducation@gmail.com
Website: www.fserc.com

Table of Contents

Modeling the Nose

Glossary of Terms

Dorsum - The anterior ridge of the nose.

Root - The concave recession located along the superior portion of the dorsum, immediately below the forehead.

Bridge - Supported by the nasal bones, the bridge forms the arched portion of the nose.

Lobe - Located along the inferior part of the dorsum, the lobe appears spherical in shape and adjoins the both the columna nasi and the wings of the nose.

Wings - Located between the nasal sulcus and the lobe of the nose, each wing lies along the inferior margin of the side of the nose.

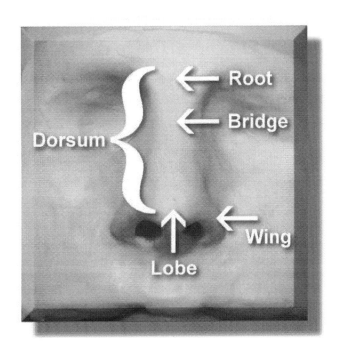

Columna Nasi - The skin partition located between the nostrils.

Glabella - Located superior to the root of the nose, the glabella is an eminence of the forehead found between the eyebrows.

Sides - Located between the bridge and each wing of the nose, the sides comprise the lateral walls.

Nasal Sulcus - The angular depression located between the anterior cheek and the wing of the nose.

Nostrils - The external openings of the nose located between the columna nasi and each wing.

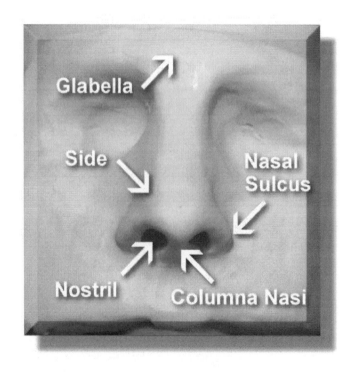

Modeling the Nose

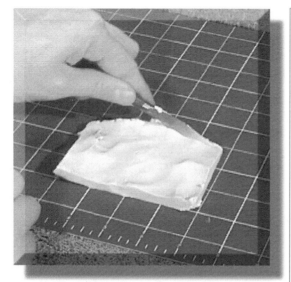

Creating the Skin

1. Create a sheet of wax approximately four inches wide and three inches long with a thickness of one-fourth inch.

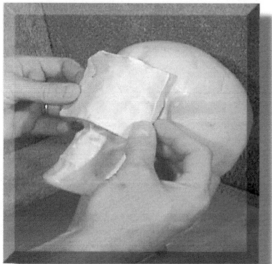

2. Place the sheet of wax on the skeletal armature covering the brow, nasal bones, eye sockets and part of the anterior cheeks.
   Do **not** completely cover the nasal spine of the maxilla.

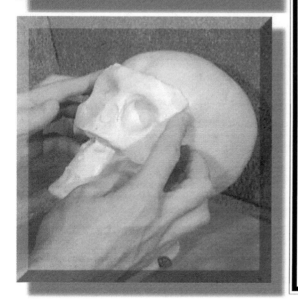

3. Anchor the wax to the skeletal armature.

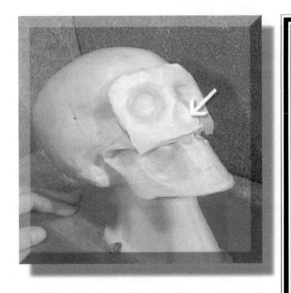

4. Flatten the wax area covering the nasal cavity.

Creating the Projection of the Nose
(bridge, lobe, tip and sides)

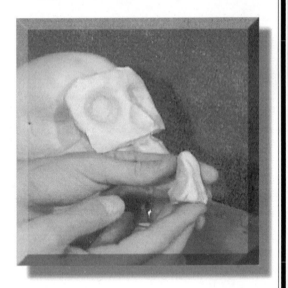

1. Create a pyramid shaped piece of wax. The size should be similar to that of your subject's nose (e.g., photograph or model).

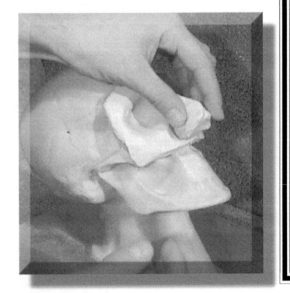

2. Attach the wax to the area covering the nasal cavity.

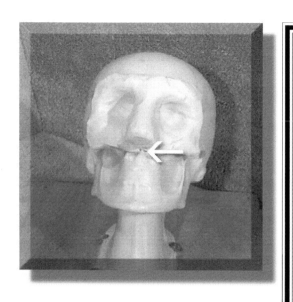

3. Again, do not completely cover the nasal spine with wax.

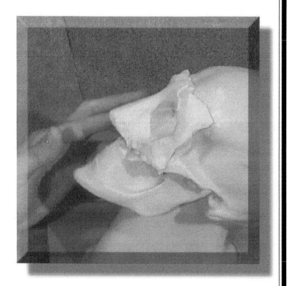

4. Blend this form into the surrounding wax.

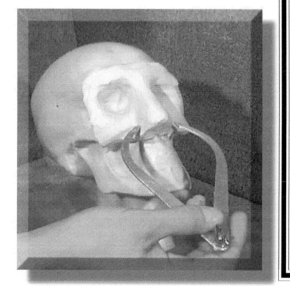

5. Compare the nose width to that of your subject's.
   Add or remove wax as needed.

5

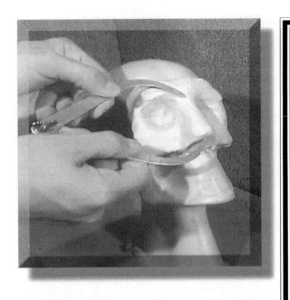

6. Compare the nose length to that of your subject's.
   Add or remove wax as needed.

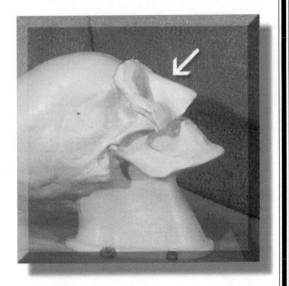

7. From the profile view, observe the inclination of the dorsum.
   Compare this to the inclination of your subject's dorsum.
   Add or remove wax as needed.

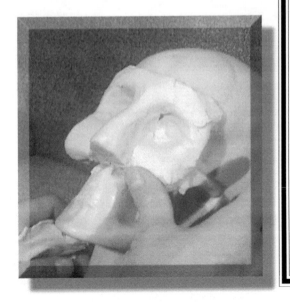

8. Add more wax to fill the anterior cheeks.

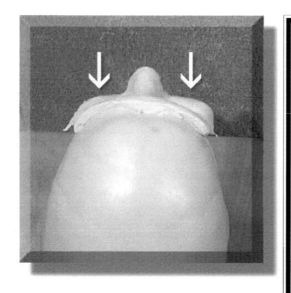

9. From the top view, inspect the anterior cheeks. Are they symmetrical? If necessary, add or remove wax.

Adding the Upper Integumentary Lip

1. Create a slip of wax representing the upper integumentary lip. The thickness of this piece should measure at least one-half inch.

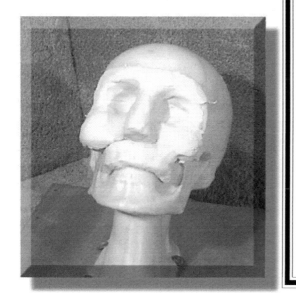

2. Place the wax along the maxilla, adjacent to (and below) the nose.

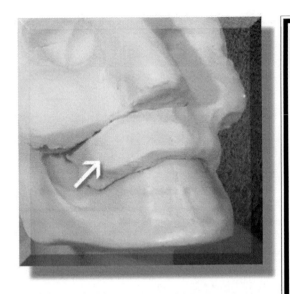

3. The upper integumentary lip is the skin region bordering the orifice of the mouth at its superior aspect.
It includes the skin area below the nose and extends to (but does not include) the

mucous membrane (red lip area).

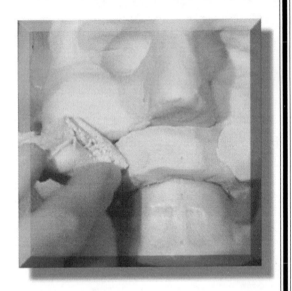

4. Add more wax to the anterior cheek areas.

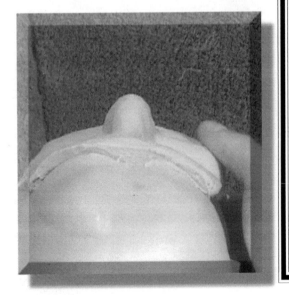

5. Again, determine symmetry of the anterior cheeks by observing the area from the top view.

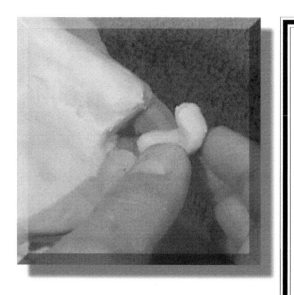

Adding the Columna Nasi and Lobe

1. Create a small piece of wax representing the columna nasi.

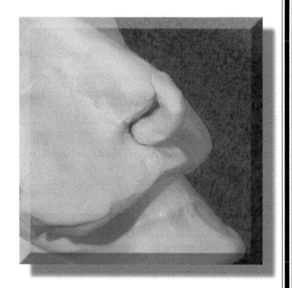

2. Add the columna nasi along the median line, as shown here.
   The columna nasi is the external skin located between the nostrils.

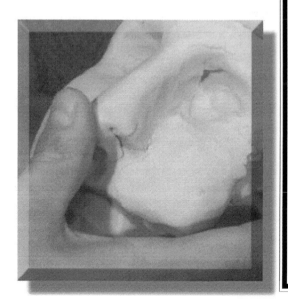

3. Blend the wax located at the lobe into the surrounding area.

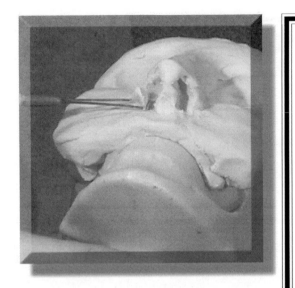

Creating the Nostrils

1. To create nostril depth, remove wax with a wire end tool. Carve to a depth of one-fourth to one-half inch. Often, the nostrils are close in proximity near the tip of the nose and further apart near the integumentary lip.

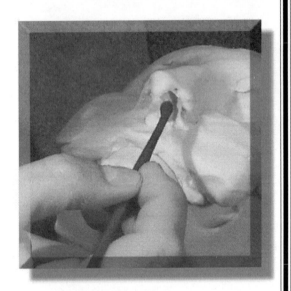

2. Increase the depth with a small to medium size round end modeling tool.

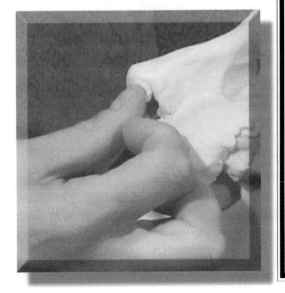

3. Add wax to the inferior margins of each wing.

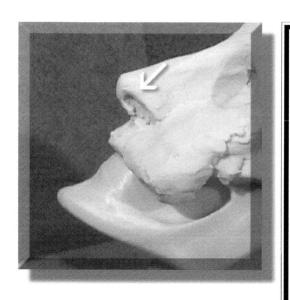

4. Normally, the inferior margin of each wing locates superior to the base of the columna nasi.

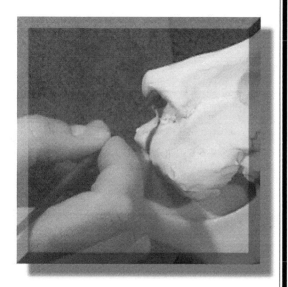

5. Blend the wax into the surrounding structures.

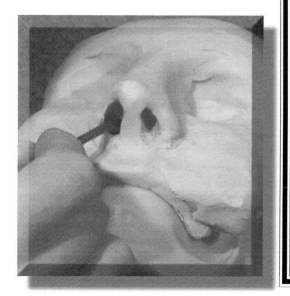

6. Smooth the margins of the columna nasi and wings.

11

Achieving Exact Duplication

Correcting size for exact duplication is time consuming. By now, you have a "rough form" of the nose. Perhaps the size of your modeled nose resembles that of your subject's. The only way to achieve exact duplication is to add, remove, or shape the wax as you observe the nose from the following views:

1. **Front View**
2. **Profile View**
3. **Bottom View (peering up toward the base of the nose)**
4. **Top View (peering down along the dorsum of the nose)**

Work through these views in sequence, beginning with the front view. This book provides a set of corrective techniques for each of the above. Often, working through the entire sequence two or three times is necessary. This is true because the shape of the nose (or a part of the nose) in one view is usually altered as the modeler changes the form when using another view.

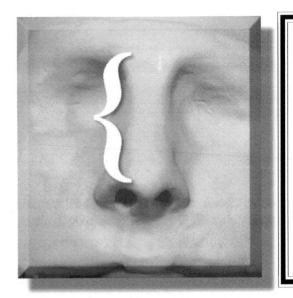

Front View

1. Determine the proper length of the dorsum from the root to the tip of the nose.
    Add or remove wax as needed.

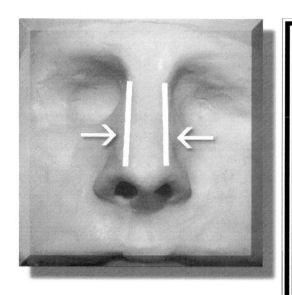

2. Determine the proper width of the dorsum.
   Add or remove wax as needed.
   Also, look for any curvature of the dorsum.

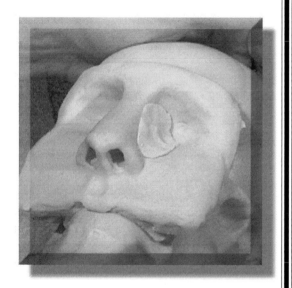

3. If necessary, add or remove wax from the sides and bridge of the nose.

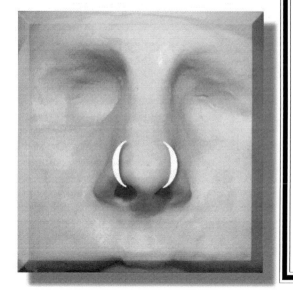

4. Measure the width of the lobe of the nose.
   Add or remove wax as needed.

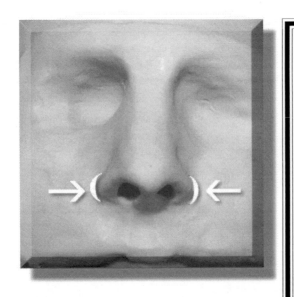

5. Measure from the lateral edge of one
   wing to the other.
   Compare the width to that of your
   subject's nose.

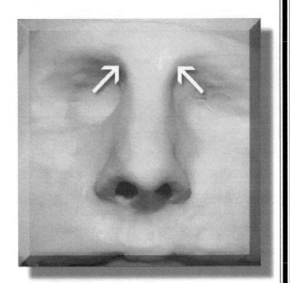

6. Shape the brows as needed.
   Look for the presence of the glabella.

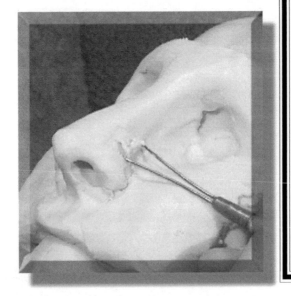

7. With a wire end tool, remove wax to
   create the depression found superior to
   each wing of the nose.

Profile View

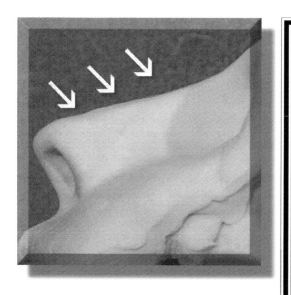

1. Observe the linear outline of the dorsum.
   Adding or removing wax may be necessary.

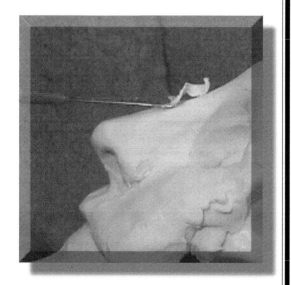

2. A wire end tool is used to remove excess wax from the dorsum.

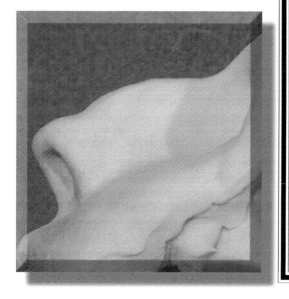

3. Wax must be added to the anterior surface of the dorsum when modeling a hooked (Roman) nose.

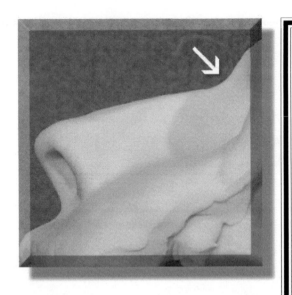

4. Determine the proper depth of the root. Add or subtract wax as needed.

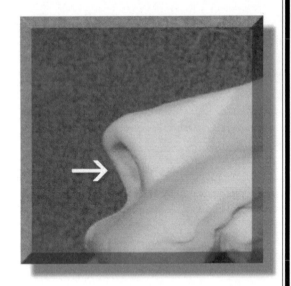

5. Inspect the columna nasi from the profile view.

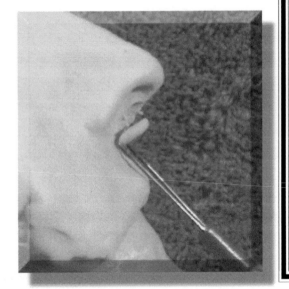

6. To create a depressed columna nasi, remove a portion of the wax with a wire end tool.

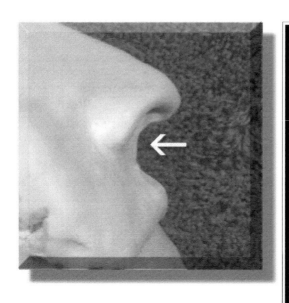

7. A depressed columna nasi is shown here.

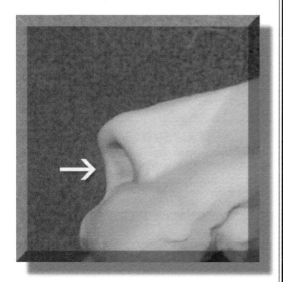

8. Here is an example of an elevated columna nasi.

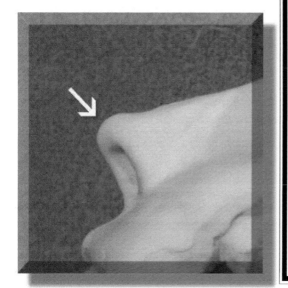

9. Inspect the linear outline of the lobe. Add or remove wax as needed.

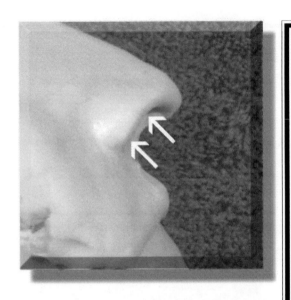

10. Determine the proper surface contour of each wing's inferior margin.

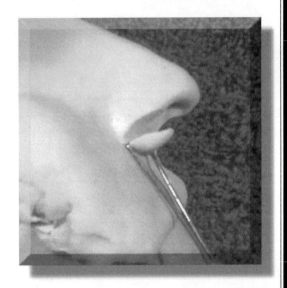

11. If necessary remove any excess wax.

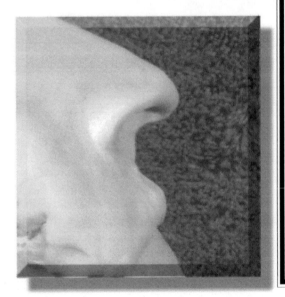

12. Then, smooth the wax.

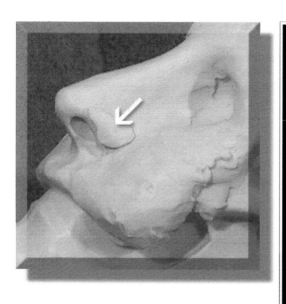

13. Adding wax to the lateral surface of each wing is sometimes required.

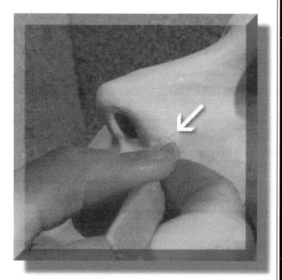

14. If necessary, the nasal sulcus is carved into the wax using a blunt modeling tool.

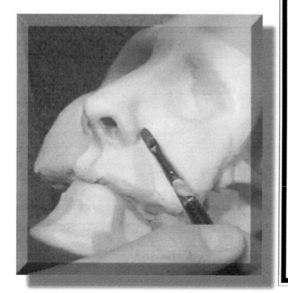

15. Here, the nasal sulcus is smoothed with a solvent (e.g., acetone) saturated brush.

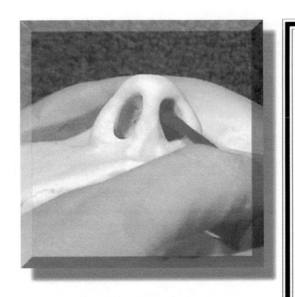

Bottom View

1. With a small round end modeling tool, shape the margins of each nostril.

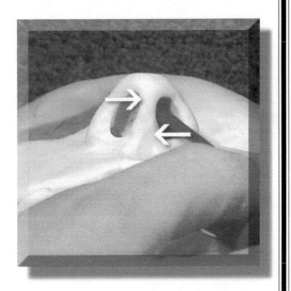

2. Often, the width of the columna nasi narrows near the lobe. (top arrow) Also, the columna nasi widens near the upper integumentary lip. (bottom arrow)

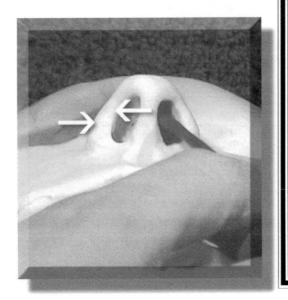

3. Inspect the thickness each wing's wall. Compare this to the wall thickness of your subject's nose.

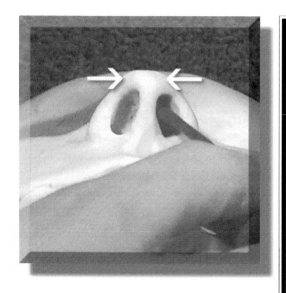

4. Add or remove wax from the lobe, as needed.

Top View

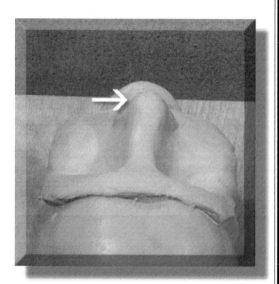

1. Observe the dorsum.
   Often, a nose will bend to one side.

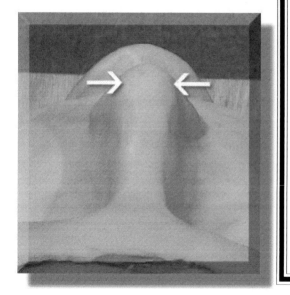

2. Inspect the shape of the lobe and tip.

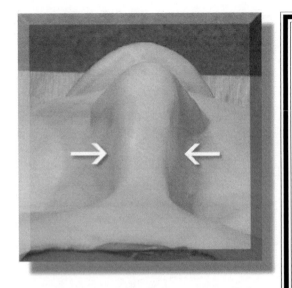

3. Add or remove wax from the sides and bridge of the nose, as needed.

Final Review

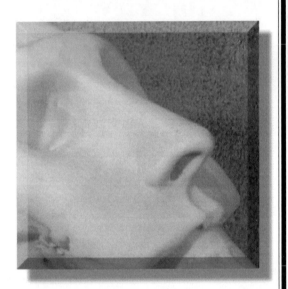

1. Review the front, profile, top, and bottom views of the nose.

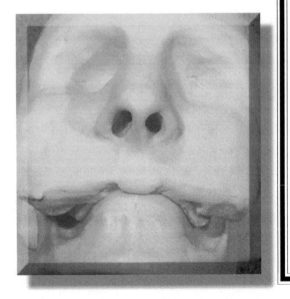

2. Make corrections as needed.

Modeling the Mouth

Glossary of Terms

Angulus Oris Eminence - The small eminence lateral and slightly superior to the corner of the mouth.

Angulus Oris Sulcus - The sulcus or furrow at the corner of the mouth. It extends from the corner both laterally and inferiorly.

Integumentary Lips -
    a) **Upper Integumentary Lip** - The skin that surrounds the orifice of the mouth region superiorly. It includes the area from the base of the nose to the upper mucous membrane.

    b) **Lower Integumentary Lip** - The skin region that surrounds the orifice of the mouth inferiorly. It includes the area from the lower mucous membrane to the labiomental sulcus.

Labiomental Sulcus - The furrow along the superior border of the chin.

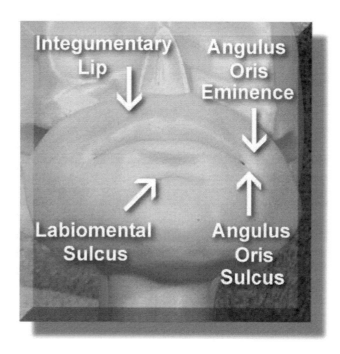

Mucous Membranes - The red surface of the lips.

Nasolabial Fold - The elevation of tissue that begins at the nasal sulcus and proceeds inferiorly and laterally to the corner of the mouth.

Nasolabial Sulcus - The furrow medially adjacent to the nasolabial fold.

Philtrum - The depression along the median line found on the upper integumentary lip.

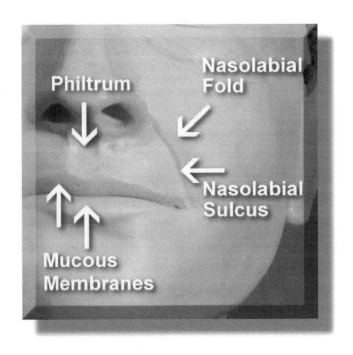

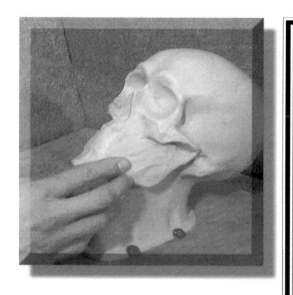

Backing/Support

1. Apply wax over the molar teeth.

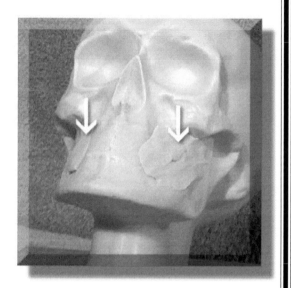

2. If your subject's face is full or heavy, add a larger volume of wax to this area. Alternately, less wax is added when duplicating the mouth of a thin subject.

Upper Mucous Membrane

1. Create a cylinder shaped piece of wax approximately one inch in diameter. This wax represents the upper mucous membrane (red lip). Make certain the wax is symmetrical in shape as you carefully smooth its surface.

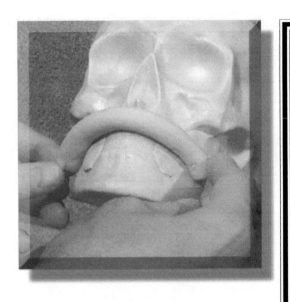

2. Place the cylinder on the skeletal armature, as shown here.
   To achieve a relaxed appearance, turn the ends downward.

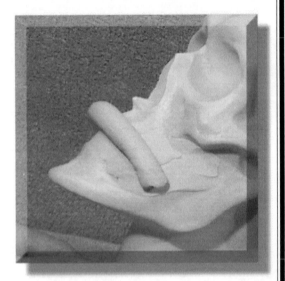

3. Normally, this cylinder covers the top row of teeth.

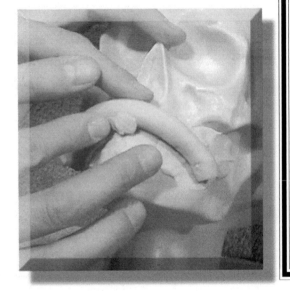

4. To create a central lobe, add a small pellet of wax on the **inferior surface** (along the median line) of the cylinder.

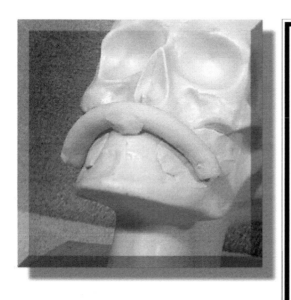

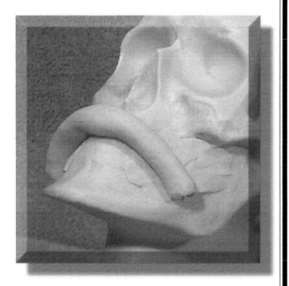

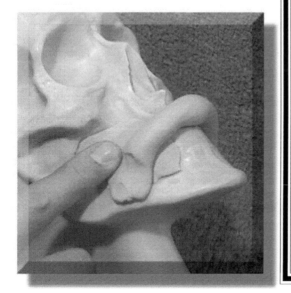

5. The size of the lobe will vary, depending upon the subject.

6. Blend the pellet of wax into the surrounding mucous membrane.

7. Anchor the ends of the cylinder to the skeletal armature.

   Note: As an option, the central lobe may be attached to the mucous membrane **before** the entire roll of wax is placed on the skeletal armature.

27

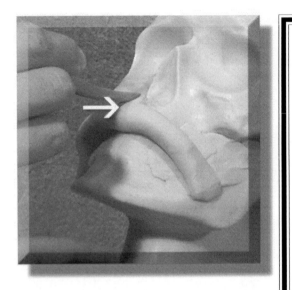

Creating the Philtrum

1. With a broad flat modeling tool, create a depression along the superior-anterior surface of the wax cylinder. This depression represents the philtrum of the upper integumentary lip.

2. The philtrum locates along the median line.
   Optionally, the depression may be created with a finger or a wire end modeling tool.

Creating the Superior Margin of the Upper Mucous Membrane

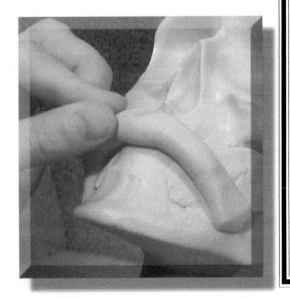

1. With your fingers, create the line of demarcation separating the mucous membrane from the integumentary lip.

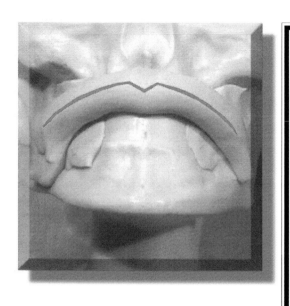

2. Here, the black line represents the superior margin of the mucous membrane.

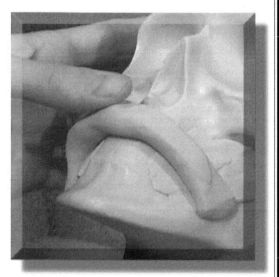

3. The line of demarcation becomes more visible as the integumentary lip is flattened.
Do not apply excessive pressure.
A light touch is all that is necessary.

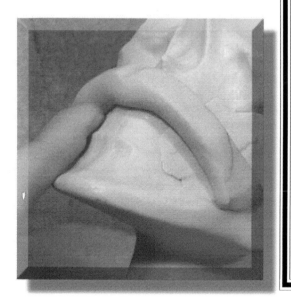

4. The rounded mucous membrane may be contoured and smoothed at this time.

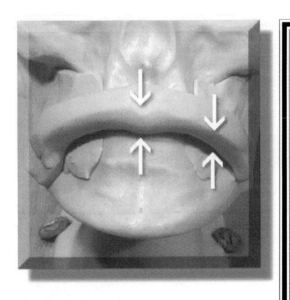

5. The thickness of the mucous membrane becomes narrow near the lateral ends (lateral arrows).
The area is relatively thick along the midline (middle arrows).

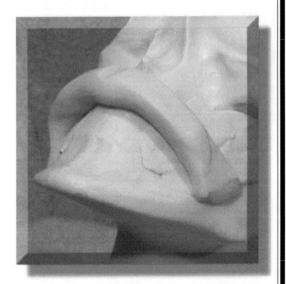

6. Often, the line of demarcation is faint and smooth (not sharp).

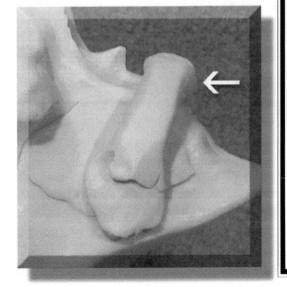

7. Notice the full curvature of the central lobe.

30

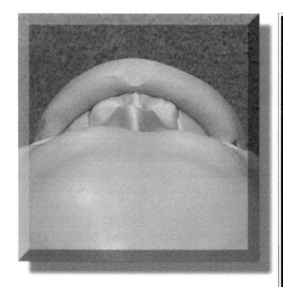

8. Inspect the upper mucous membrane. Is it symmetrical?

Adding the Upper Integumentary Lip

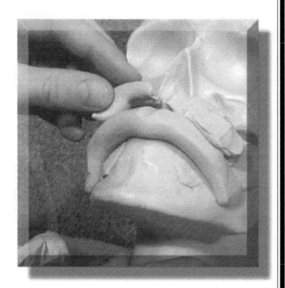

1. To create the remainder of the upper integumentary lip, add a sufficient amount of wax to the area immediately superior to the upper lip.

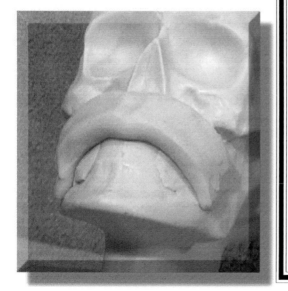

2. Blend together both pieces of wax.

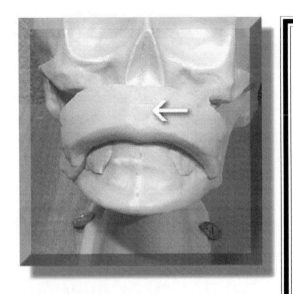

3. Extend the philtrum into the upper integumentary lip.

The Lower Mucous Membrane

1. Create a cylinder of wax representing the lower mucous membrane. The diameter is slightly **less** than that of the previous cylinder.

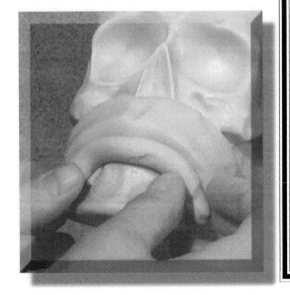

2. Place the cylinder of wax below the upper mucous membrane, as shown here.

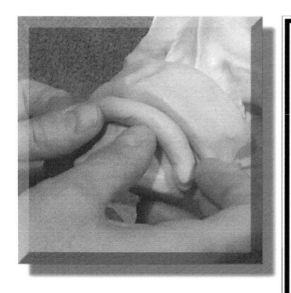

3. Push the cylinder toward the upper mucous membrane.
   Here, the mouth's line of closure is created.

4. At each end, anchor the cylinder to the skeletal armature.

Creating the Inferior Margin of the Mucous Membrane

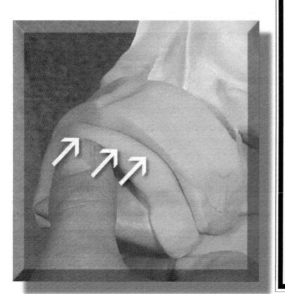

1. With your fingers, create the line of demarcation separating the mucous membrane from the integumentary lip.

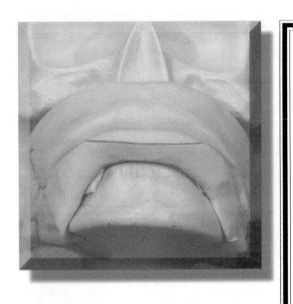

2. Here, the black line represents the inferior margin of the mucous membrane.

3. At the midline, mark the thickness of the mucous membrane by depressing the wax with your thumb.

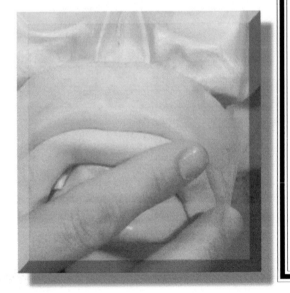

4. While moving in a lateral direction, depress the wax with your finger or thumb to create the line of demarcation. Again, do **not** apply excessive pressure.

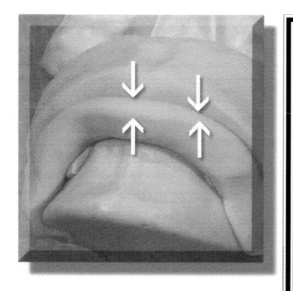

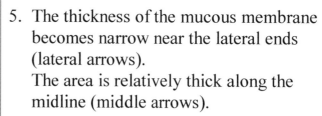

5. The thickness of the mucous membrane becomes narrow near the lateral ends (lateral arrows).
   The area is relatively thick along the midline (middle arrows).

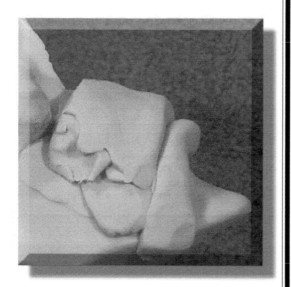

6. From the profile view, inspect the fullness of the mucous membrane. Compare this to the fullness of your subject's bottom lip.

Adding the Lower Integumentary Lip

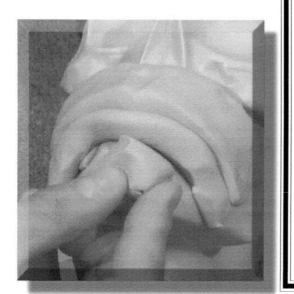

1. Create the remainder of the lower integumentary lip by adding a sufficient amount of wax to the area above the chin.

35

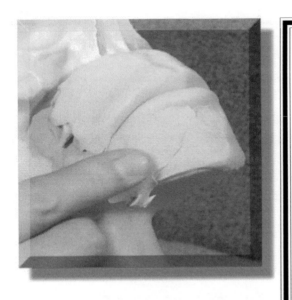

2. Additional wax is added to create parts of the anterior and lateral cheeks.

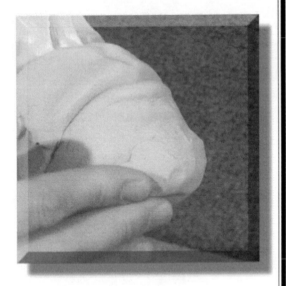

3. Wax is added to create the prominence of the chin.

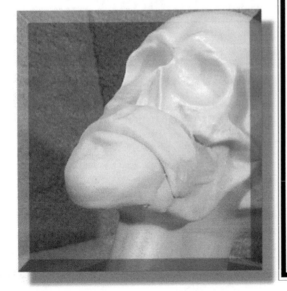

4. Compare the size and shape of the chin to that of your subject's.

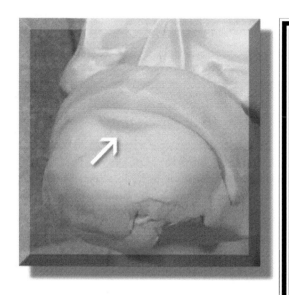

5. Inspect the depression found below the lower lip.
   The depth varies among different subjects.

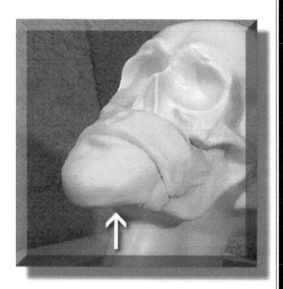

6. If necessary, add more wax to the area located below the chin and mandible.

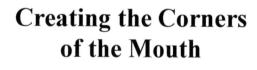

Creating the Corners of the Mouth

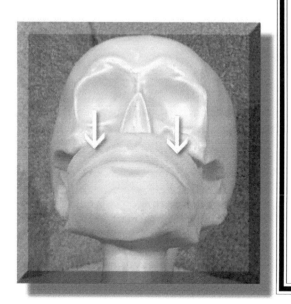

1. Normally, each mouth corner will align vertically with the center of the eye above it.

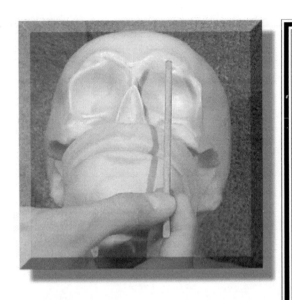

2. Align a straight modeling tool over the center of each eye to determine the location of the mouth corners. Mark each corner with a slight depression.

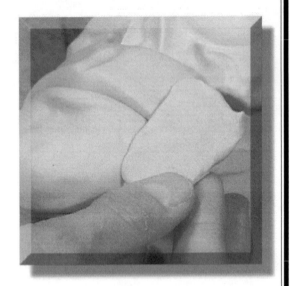

3. Place a small sheet of wax lateral to each corner.

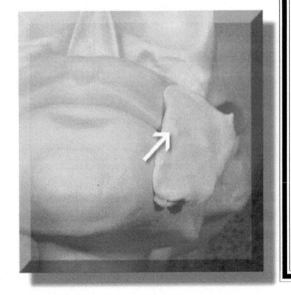

4. This wax contributes to the fullness of the angulus oris eminence and cheek.

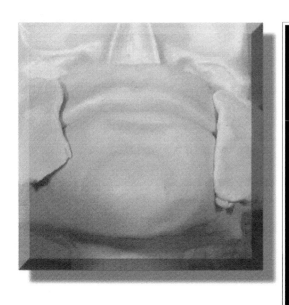

5. Here, the wax additions define the location of the mouth corners.

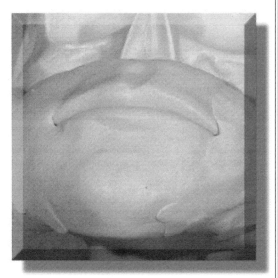

6. Blend the wax into the surrounding integumentary lips and cheeks.

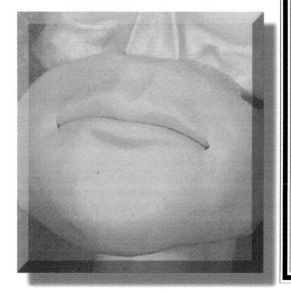

7. All but the immediate corners are smoothed.

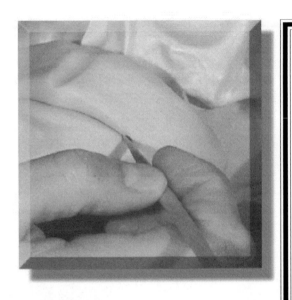

8. With a flat end modeling tool, blend the wax at each corner into the mucous membranes.

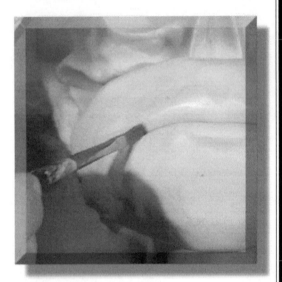

9. A solvent saturated flat brush will help smooth each corner.

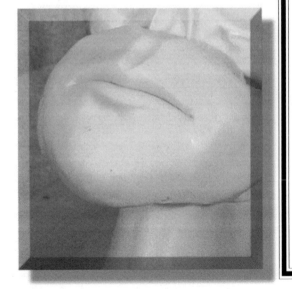

10. Inspect the corners of the mouth. Compare them to the corners of your subject's mouth.

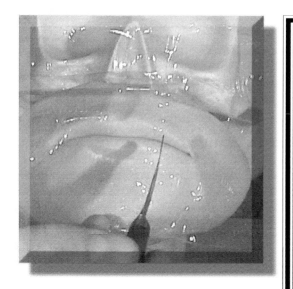

Creating Facial Markings

1. Vertical lines found on mucous membranes are carved with a spatula. To create soft margins, plastic or wax paper is first applied to the lip surfaces.

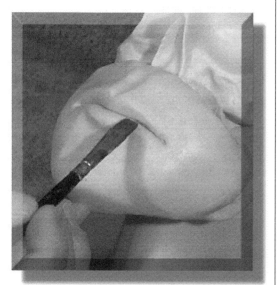

2. Remaining sharp lines are smoothed with a solvent saturated flat brush.

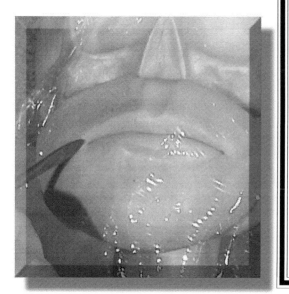

3. The angulus oris sulcus is made using the same method.
   Here, a flat wooden modeling tool creates a faint depression located lateral and below each corner.

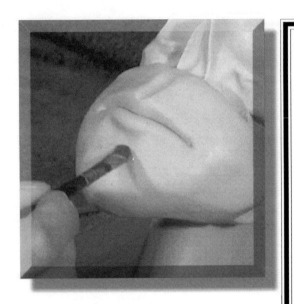

4. Here, the labiomental sulcus is created. It locates along the superior border of the chin.

A Final Check of Size and Form

Inspect your work from the profile, front, top, and bottom views. The following checklist should help you achieve exact duplication of your subject's mouth.

Profile View

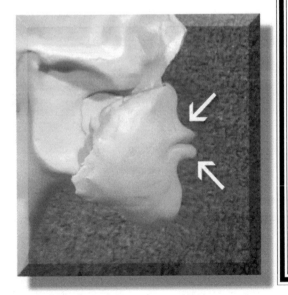

1. Observe the anterior projection of the **mucous membranes** beyond the integumentary lips.
   If they protrude too far, more wax must be added to the integumentary lips.

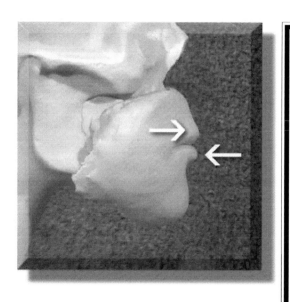

2. Compare the central projection of both lips (along the median line). On a convex facial profile, the projection of the upper mucous membane (top arrow) is slightly more anterior than the lower mucous membrane (lower arrow).

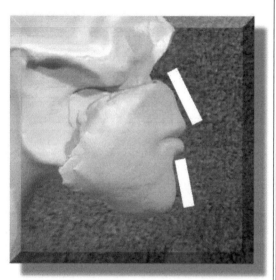

3. Determine the proper inclination of both integumentary lips. Here, both integumentary lips appear inclined.

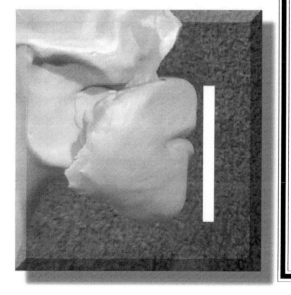

4. Here, the inclination of both integumentary lips appears vertical.

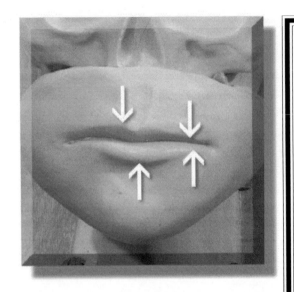

Front View

1. Inspect the fullness of each mucous membrane, beginning at the median line and progressing laterally to each corner.

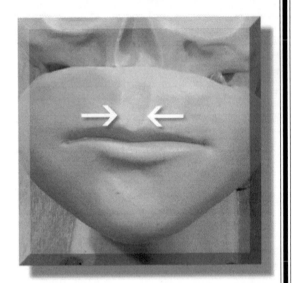

2. Survey the shape of the philtrum. Also, check the depth of its depression.

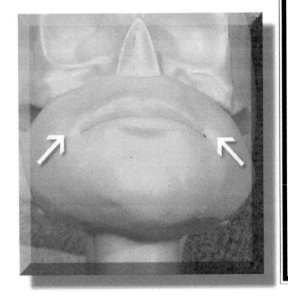

3. Look for the fullness of each angulus oris eminence.

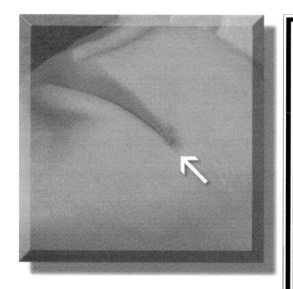

4. Check each corner for depth and smoothness.

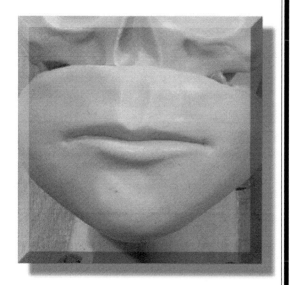

5. Inspect the line of closure of the mouth.
Does the mouth appear relaxed?

Top View

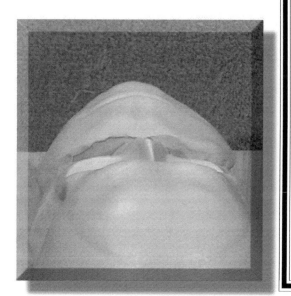

1. Observe the symmetry (or asymmetry) of both lips.

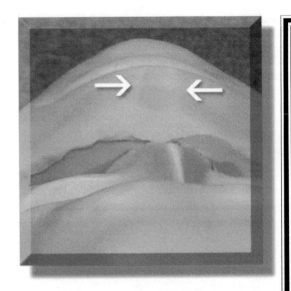

2. Observe the location of the philtrum. Does it lie along the median line of the face?

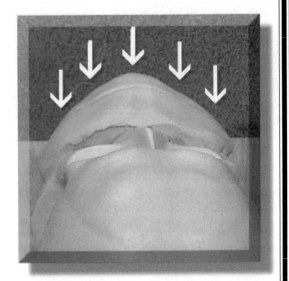

3. Observe the convex shape of the mouth.
   Does it appear too flat (wide) or too convex (narrow)?

Bottom View

From the bottom view, observe symmetry (or asymmetry) of both lips. Also, check the convex shape of the mouth.

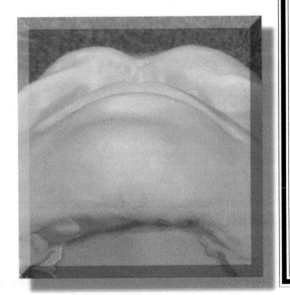

Adding the Nasolabial Fold

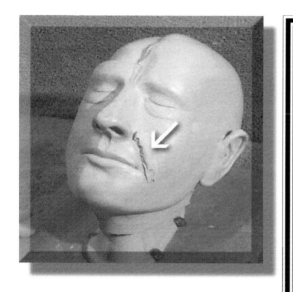

1. Place a flat piece of wax on the anterior cheek, lateral to the corner of the mouth.

 This wax represents the nasolabial fold.

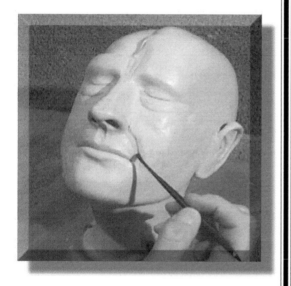

2. With a small rounded modeling tool, attach the wax to the upper integumentary lip.

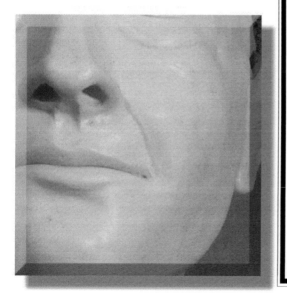

3. Notice how the nasolabial sulcus runs along the length of the medial margin of the nasolabial fold.

Modeling the Eyes

Glossary of Terms

Interciliary Sulci - Vertical or horizontal sulci located between the eyebrows.

Line of Closure - The line formed between the two closed eyelids.

Medial Canthus - Inner canthus; the medial corner of the eye.

Naso-Orbital Fossa - The depression located medial and superior to the inner canthus.

Oblique Palpebral Sulcus - The oblique furrow decending from the medial canthus and extending to a point below the middle of the eye.

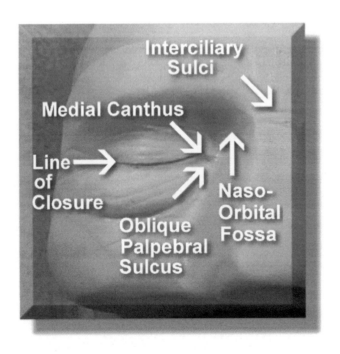

Optic Facial Sulci - Crow's feet; sulci found lateral to the outer corner of the eye.

Orbital Pouch - A fold of skin located below the lower eyelid.

Palpebra - Eyelid.

Superior Palpebral Sulcus - A furrow located along the superior border of the upper eyelid.

Supra-Orbital Area - The area located above the upper eyelid and below the eyebrow.

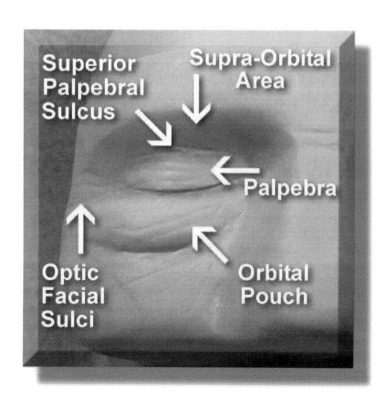

Creating the Eyes

1. Create a ball of wax for each eye. The diameter of each ball should measure appoximately one inch.

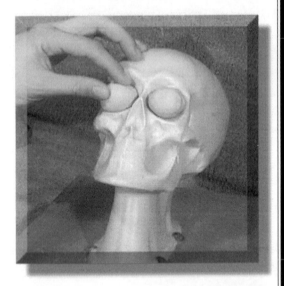

2. Place a ball of wax in each eye socket of the skeletal armature.

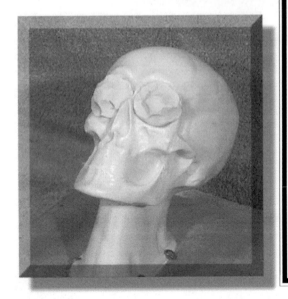

3. Attach the wax to the margins of the bony eye sockets.

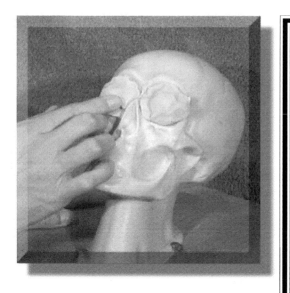

4. Flatten and smooth the remaining stalk of wax.
   Do this for each eye.

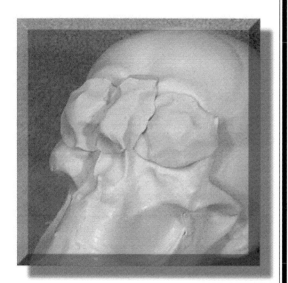

Creating the Width of the Nose

Attach wax to the surface of the armature's nasal bones. This wax represents the width of the nose.

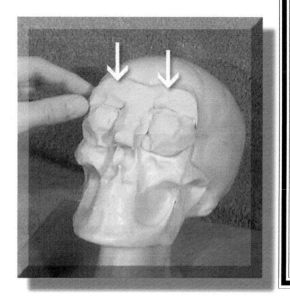

Creating the Brows

Attach wax along the inferior margin of the armature's frontal bone.

Creating the Cheeks

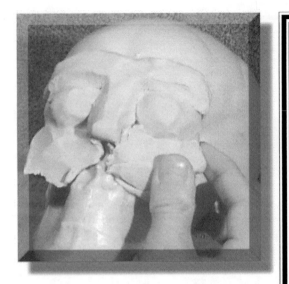

1. To create the anterior and lateral cheeks,
   attach wax to the bony surface below each eye.

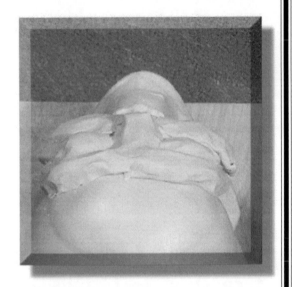

2. Symmetry of the cheeks is determined by observing the armature from the top view.
   Add or remove wax as needed.

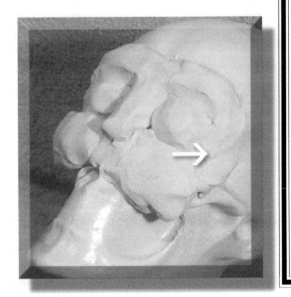

3. Attach wax to the lateral side of each eye.

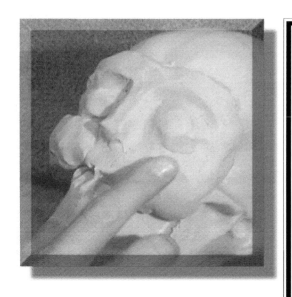

4. Smooth all wax representing the eyes, cheeks, and forehead.

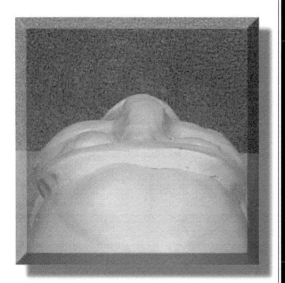

5. Again, check for symmetry of the eyes, cheeks, and forehead.

Projection of the Eye

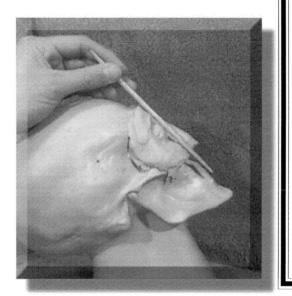

1. To determine the proper projection of the eye, place a straight modeling tool on the eyebrow and anterior cheek.

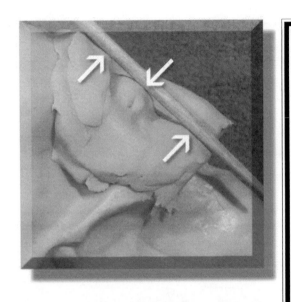

2. Normally, the eye will touch a straight modeling tool as the instrument rests in the position shown here. Exceptions to this rule exist.

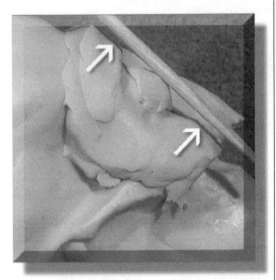

3. If the eye projects too far, the modeling tool does not rest upon the brow and anterior cheek.

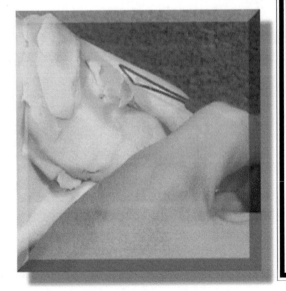

4. To correct this problem (# 3), remove wax from the anterior surface of the eye.

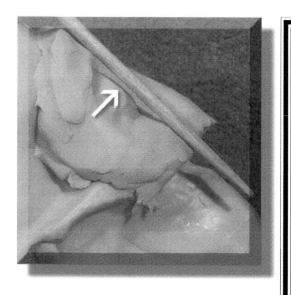

5. On some subjects, the eye may not project forward enough to touch the straight modeling tool.
This may be normal.

Shaping the Eyelids

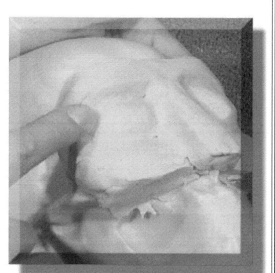

1. With your finger, manipulate the wax representing the eyes to create a normal shape.

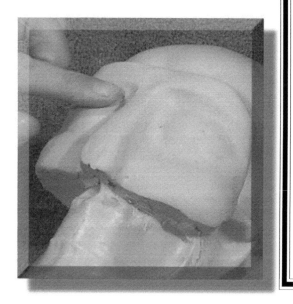

2. Blend the wax into the brow and cheeks.

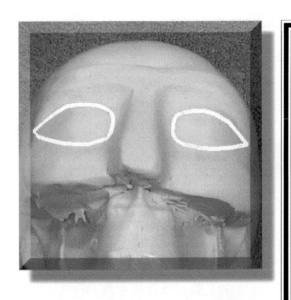

3. Normally, the shape of the eyelid (palpebra) resembles that of an almond.

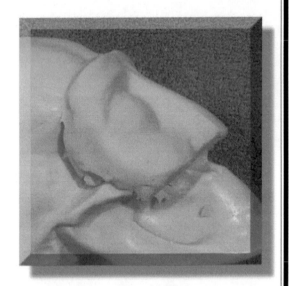

4. Observe the eyelids from the profile view.

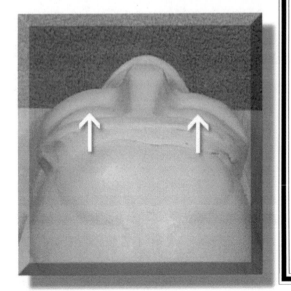

5. Observe the eyelids from the top view. The center (anterior projection) of both eyes should appear to "look" forward.

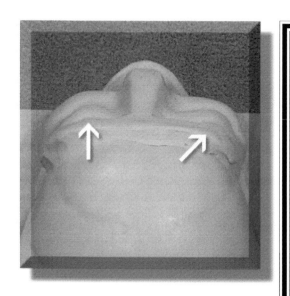

6. Here, the eyes appear to "look" in different directions.
   This is **not** normal and should be corrected.

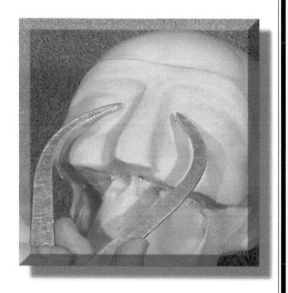

7. When shaping the eyelids, be aware that the distance between the eyes is equal to one eye width.

Creating the Line of Closure

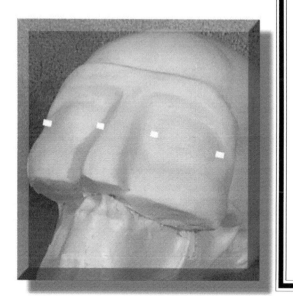

1. Before the lines of eye closure are carved, determine the location of both medial and lateral canthi.
   Mark each canthus with a slight depression.

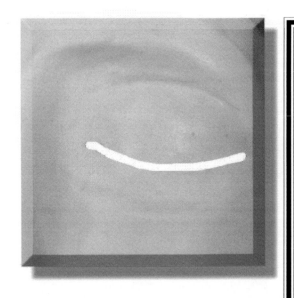

2. The line of closure locates along the lower one-third of the closed eye.

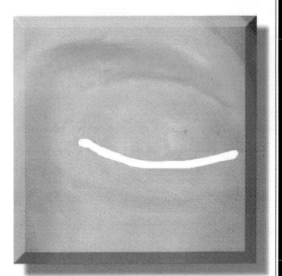

3. Normally, the line forms an inferior arc. Often, the medial canthus locates superior to the lateral canthus.

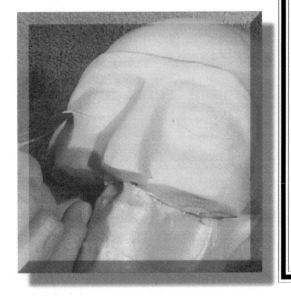

4. With a spatula, carve each closure line.

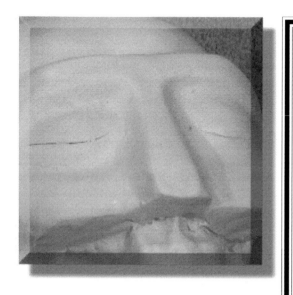

5. Compare each line for symmetry. If the lines are asymmetrical, remove and begin again.

Adjusting the Lower Eyelid

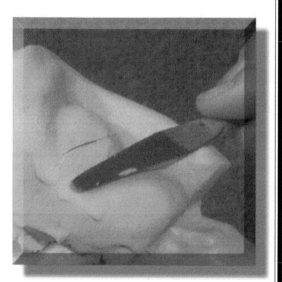

1. Scrape away some of the wax representing the lower eyelid. Remove approximately one-sixteenth of an inch thickness.

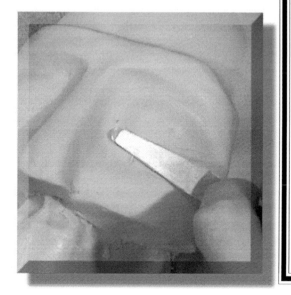

2. Beginning at the line of closure, scrape in an inferior direction along the entire length of the eye (from the medial to the lateral canthus).

3. With your finger, smooth the lower eyelid.

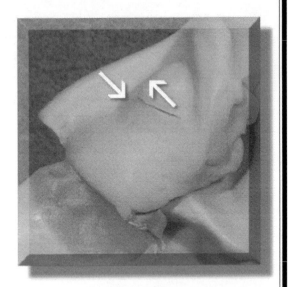

4. The upper eyelid exhibits slightly more anterior projection than the lower eyelid.

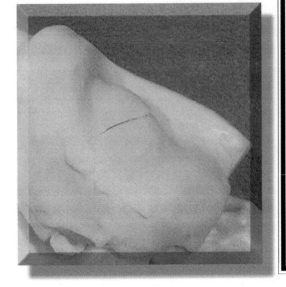

5. Be certain that both eyes appear symmetrical.

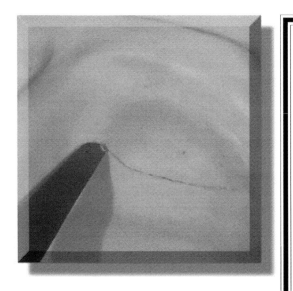

6. With a spatula or flat modeling tool, depress the wax located medial to the line of closure.
   This creates the inner canthus.

Supraorbital Area

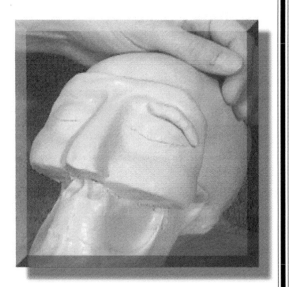

1. If necessary, duplicate the fullness of the supraorbital area by adding a cylinder of wax above each eye.

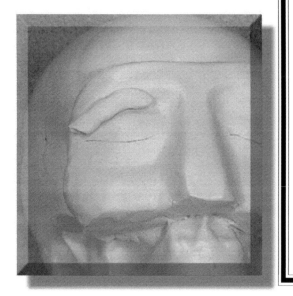

2. Here, the cylinder of wax covers only the lateral two-thirds of the supraorbital area.

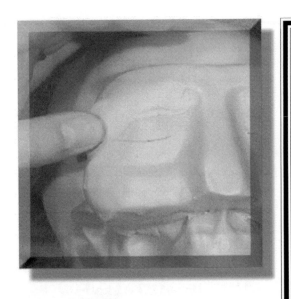

3. Blend the wax into the surrounding area.

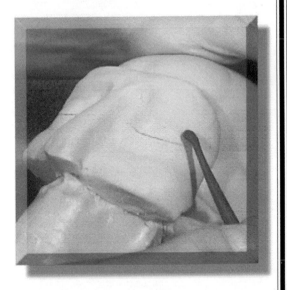

4. A round end modeling tool blends the wax of the supraorbital area into the upper eyelid.

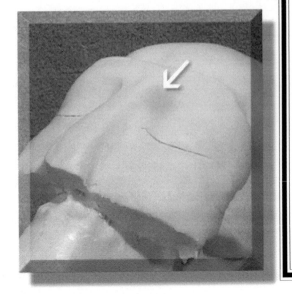

5. Determine the proper depth of the naso-orbital fossa.

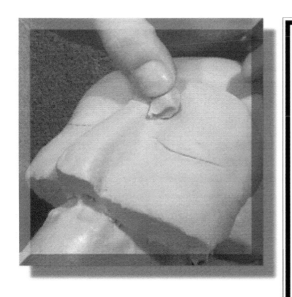

6. If necessary, wax is added to decrease the depth of the naso-orbital fossa.

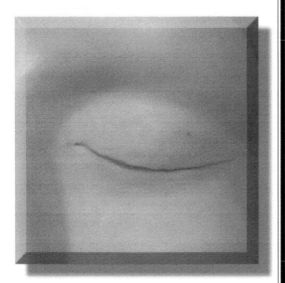

7. All edges of the supraorbital area are blended into the surrounding structures.

Filling Depressions Below the Eye

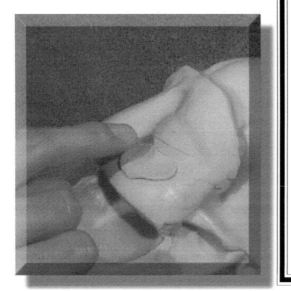

1. To fill unnatural depressions, attach additional wax to the area below each eye.

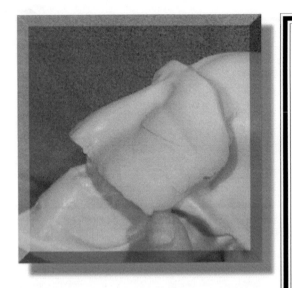

2. Blend this wax into the surrounding structures.

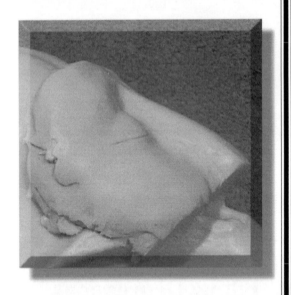

3. Using the profile view, compare both eyes for symmetry.

Moving the Supraorbital Margin

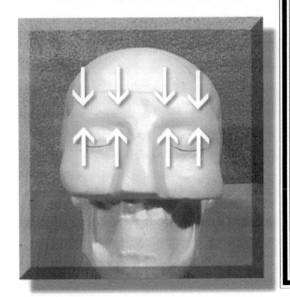

1. Sometimes the supraorbital margin locates closer to the eye.
   Thus, it becomes necessary to shift the location of the margin in an inferior direction.

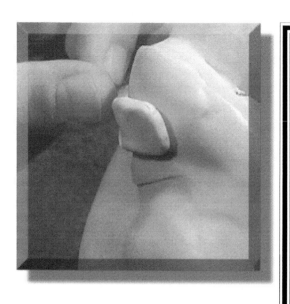

2. Here, wax is added to the inferior portion of the supraorbital margin.

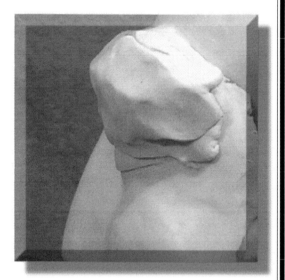

3. The anterior projection of the margin may be increased, as well.

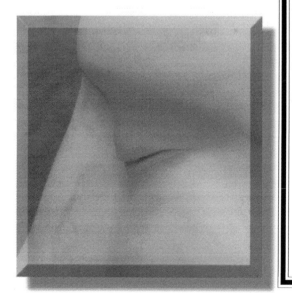

4. The margin is blended into the surrounding area, then smoothed.

65

5. The brows now locate closer to the eyes.

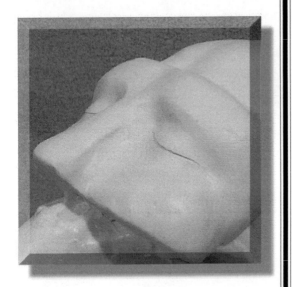

6. Observe the appearance of the eyes from a three-quarter view.

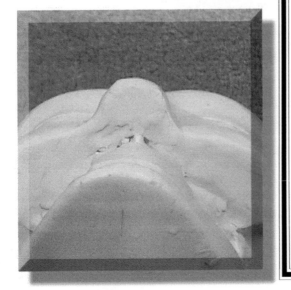

7. Observe the eyebrows from the bottom view. Are they symmetrical?

Creating Facial Markings

Determine the necessity of adding acquired and natural facial markings to your work. Create them as needed. Below are examples of the most common facial markings.

Optic Facial Sulci

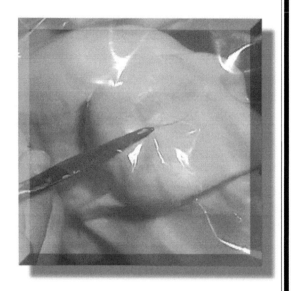

1. First, apply a thin sheet of clear plastic over the outer corner of the eye. Next, carve optic facial sulci into the wax.

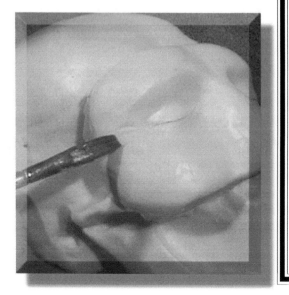

2. Using light pressure, smooth the area with a solvent saturated brush.

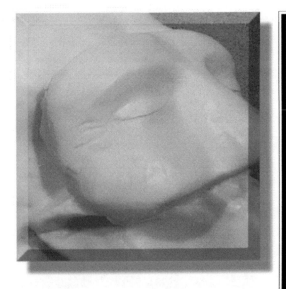

3. Normally, optic facial sulci radiate laterally from the outer corner of the eye.

Oblique Palpebral Sulcus

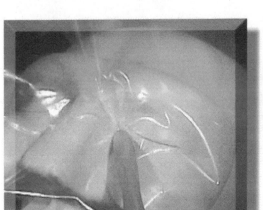

1. Again, apply plastic over the eye. Beginning below the medial canthus, apply light pressure with a flat modeling tool. Continue this pressure as you slide the tool in an inferior and lateral direction. Stop below the center of the eye.

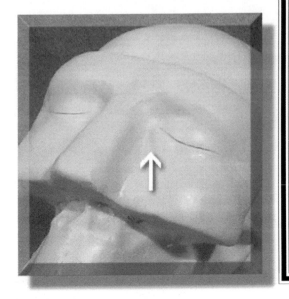

2. Notice the slightly shadowed appearance of this broad and shallow sulcus.

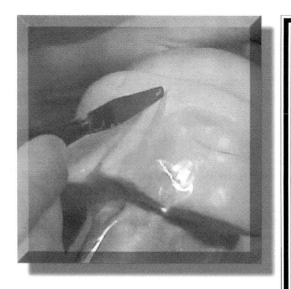

Interciliary Sulci

1. Vertical interciliary sulci are made by carving lines above the root of the nose and between the eyebrows.

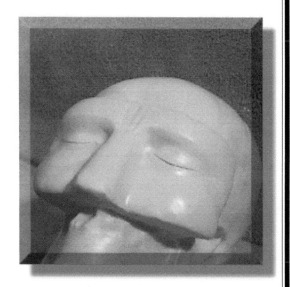

2. The length and depth of each sulcus may vary.

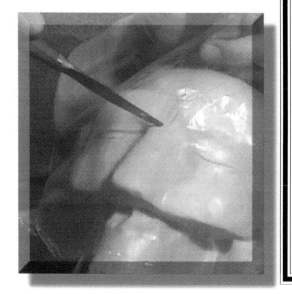

3. Transverse interciliary sulci locate on the anterior surface of the root of the nose.

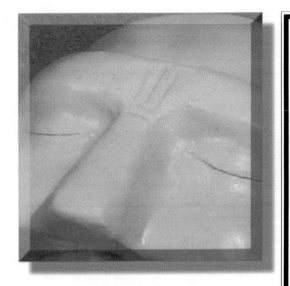

4. Again, length and depth may vary.

Orbital Pouch

1. First, apply a thin piece of wax beneath each lower eyelid.
   A large puffy pouch requires a thicker piece of wax.

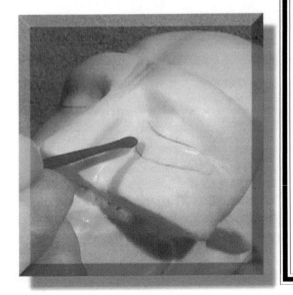

2. With a round end modeling tool, attach the inferior margin of the orbital pouch to the cheek surface.

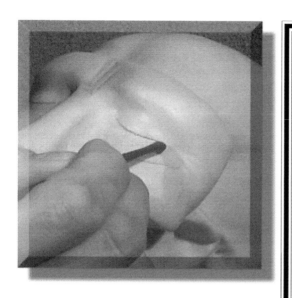

3. Next, attach the superior margin of the pouch to the lower eyelid.

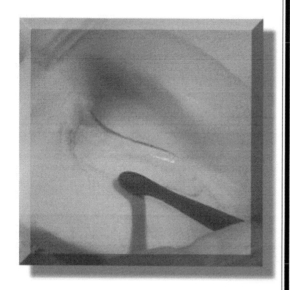

4. Carefully blend the margins into the surrounding wax.

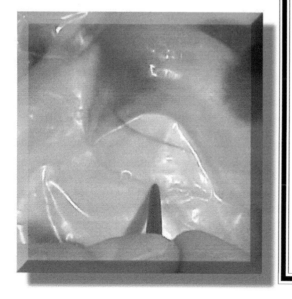

5. Apply clear plastic to the area. Carve the lower sulcus with a sharp modeling tool.

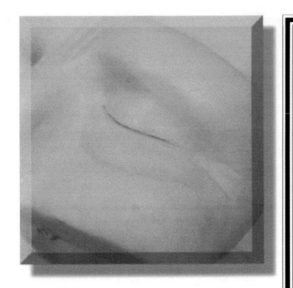

6. Remove the plastic. Inspect your work.

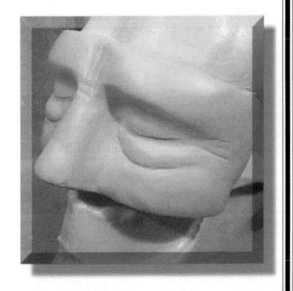

7. Observe both eyes. Are they symmetrical?

Superior Palpebral Sulcus

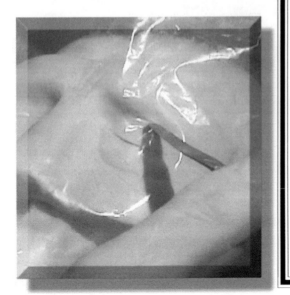

1. With a spatula, carve the superior palpebral sulcus.
    This sulcus locates where the upper eyelid attaches to the supraorbital area.

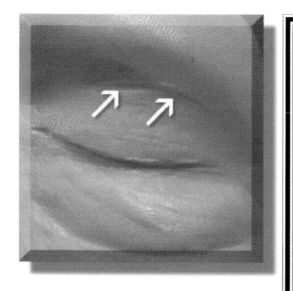

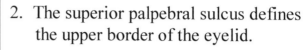
2. The superior palpebral sulcus defines the upper border of the eyelid.

Common Transverse Sulcus & Linear Sulci

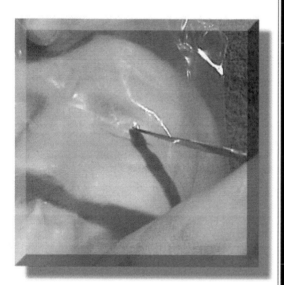
1. With a spatula, carve furrows that appear on the eyelids.

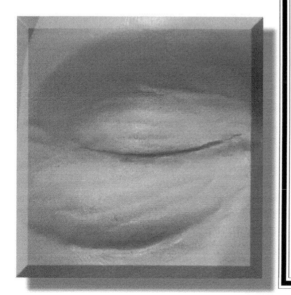
2. Here is a closer look at these furrows.

A Final Check
of Size and Form

Inspect your work from the profile, front, top, and bottom views. To acheive exact duplication of your subject's eyes, follow the checklist below.

Profile View

1. Observe the profile silhouette of the supraorbital area, upper eyelid, and lower eyelid.
   Each should form a convex arc.

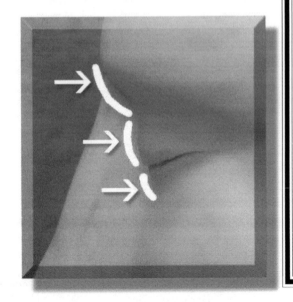

2. The arc of the upper eyelid posteriorly recedes from that of the supraorbital area.
   Similarly, arc of the lower eyelid posteriorly recedes from that of the upper eyelid.

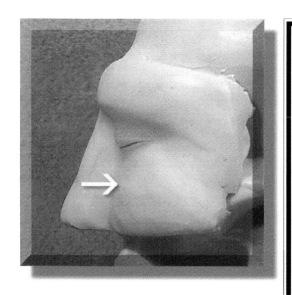

3. Observe the anterior projection of the cheekbone.

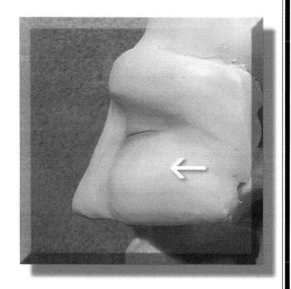

4. Here, the cheekbone appears full as it projects anteriorly.
   In some cases, the cheekbone may posteriorly recede.

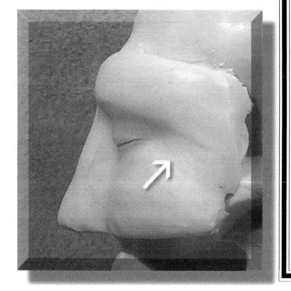

5. Observe the area lateral to the eye corner.

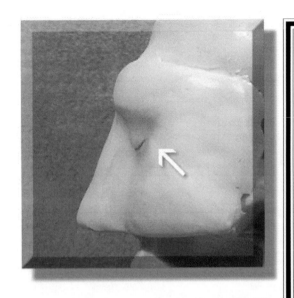

6. Compared to the previous photograph, this area is shaped differently.
This may be normal for some subjects.

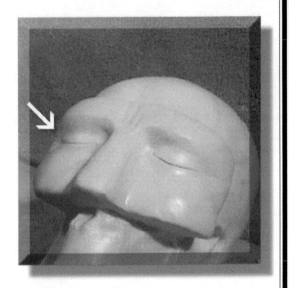

7. The three quarter view is valuable for inspecting the area lateral to the eye corner.

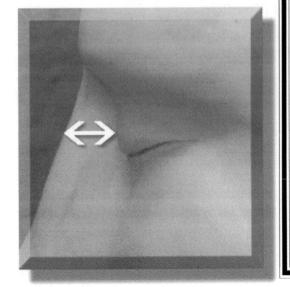

8. Determine the proper distance between the anterior margins of the nose and the upper eyelid.

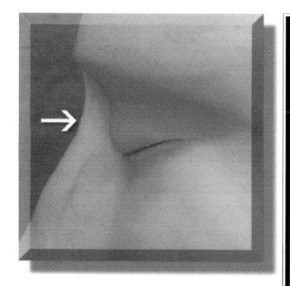

9. Compared to the previous photograph, this distance measures less. It will vary among different subjects

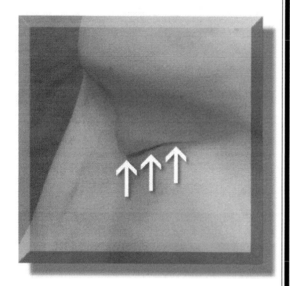

10. From the profile view, the line of eye closure appears gently curved.

Front View

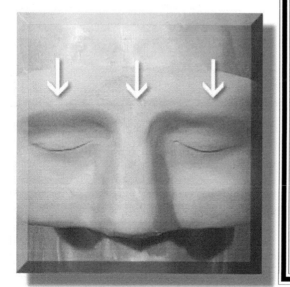

1. Inspect the supraorbital margin.

2. Compared to the previous photograph, the appearance of the subject is changed by altering the supraorbital margin.

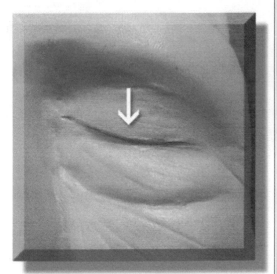

3. Normally, the line of eye closure exhibits an inferior arc.
   This form will vary among subjects.

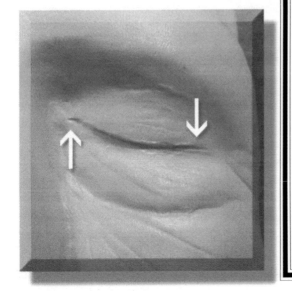

4. Often, the medial canthus locates superior to the lateral canthus.
   Exceptions to this rule exist.

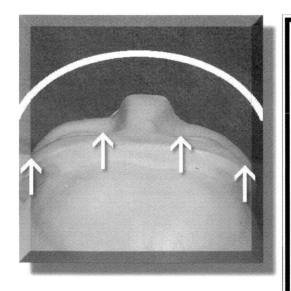

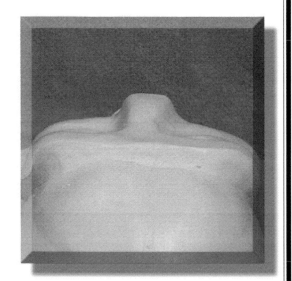

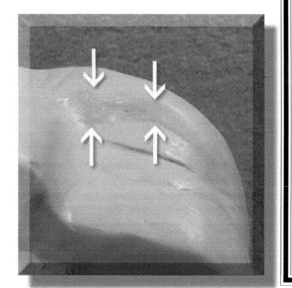

Top View

1. Due to the bilateral curvature of the head, the lateral corners of the eyes locate posterior to the medial corners.

2. Without bilateral curvature, the structures surrounding the eyes appear unnaturally flat across the width of the face.

Bottom View

1. Inspect the anterior projection of the brows.

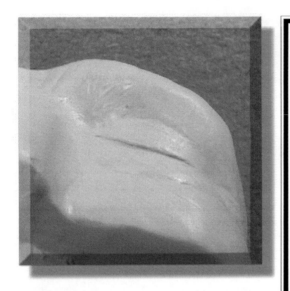

2. The brow anteriorly projects beyond
   the eyes.
   Evaluate the degree of projection for
   each individual subject.

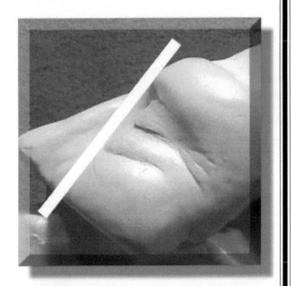

3. The profile view is helpful when
   determining the anterior projection
   of the eye.

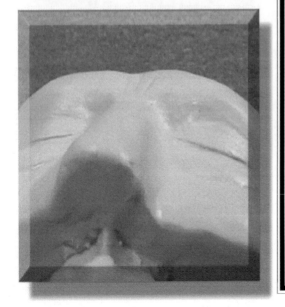

4. Observe both brows to evaluate
   symmetry.

80

Modeling the Ear

Glossary of Terms

Depressions:

Auditory Meatus - Ear passage.

Concha - The depression located superior, posterior, and inferior to the ear passage.

Intertragic Notch - The notch located between the tragus and antitragus.

Scapha - The long, slender depression located between the helix and antihelix.

Triangular Fossa - The depression located between the crura of the antihelix.

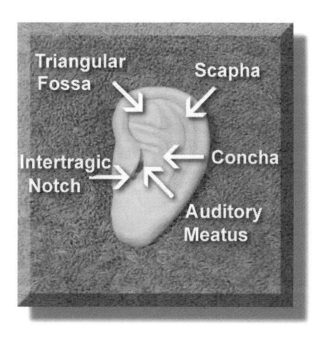

Elevations:

Antihelix - The inner rim of the ear located adjacent to the scapha.

Antitragus - The eminence located superior to the lobe of the ear and posterior to the intertragic notch.

Helix - The outer rim of the ear.

Lobe - The rounded portion of skin located inferior to the concha.

Tragus - The prominence located anterior to the auditory meatus.

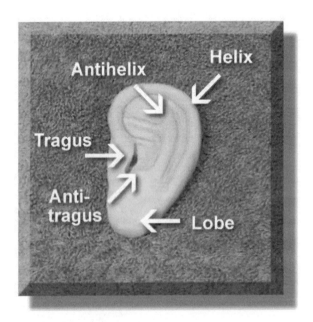

Several methods of modeling the ear exist. The method demonstrated in this manual may or may not be suited to each restorative artist.

Creating the Wedge

Create a wedge of wax measuring approximately two and one-half inches wide and three inches long.

Carving the Concha

1. With a small round end modeling tool, depress the wax to create the auditory meatus.
   This depression locates toward the anterior (thin side) margin of the wedge.

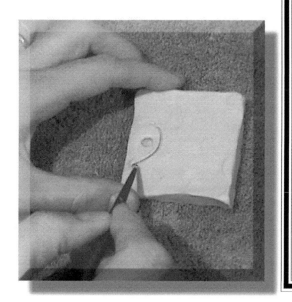

2. Carve the outline of the concha.

3. Using a wire end tool, remove wax to create the concha
Follow the outline you previously made. Observe the depth of your subject's ear. Carve at the same depth.

4. Smooth the area with a round end modeling tool.

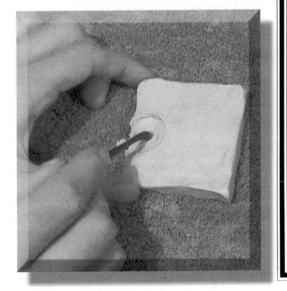

5. If necessary, re-create the auditory meatus.

Carving the Triangular Fossa

1. Carve the outline of the triangular fossa. The size and shape of the fossa should duplicate that of your subject's ear.

2. With a wire end tool, remove the necessary amount of wax inside of the drawn outline.

3. Smooth the triangular fossa with a small round end modeling tool.

Carving the Scapha

1. Carve the outline of the scapha. Start above the triangular fossa and progress downward toward the lobe of the ear.

2. Remove the necessary amount of wax along the drawn outline.

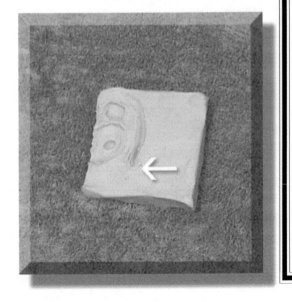

3. Often, the scapha terminates slightly below the ear passage.

4. Smooth the scapha with a small round end modeling tool.

Removing Excess Wax

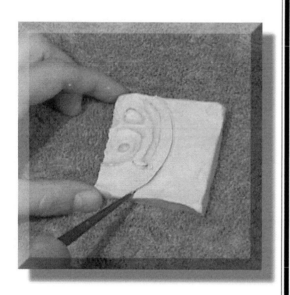

1. Detemine the location and shape of the ear's outer rim.
   Draw an outline with a sharp modeling tool.

2. Beginning at a superior position, carve away excess wax.
   Leave a ridge of wax outside of the scapha.

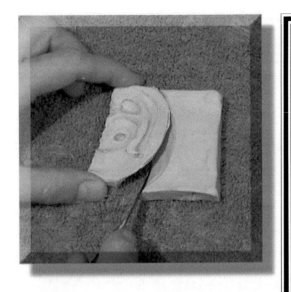

3. Carve through the entire thickness of the wax and remove the excess.

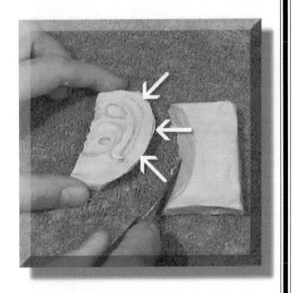

4. Inspect the ridge of wax. This ridge forms the helix.

Shaping the Helix

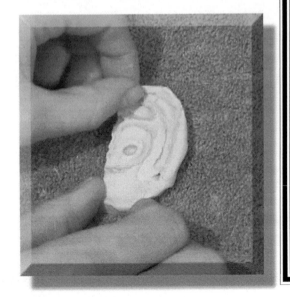

1. With your fingertips, shape the anterior-superior part of the helix.

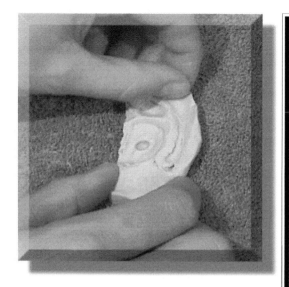

2. Smooth the ridge along the top and back side of the ear.

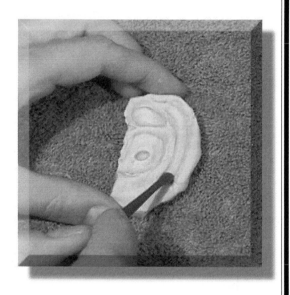

3. Use a small round end modeling tool to smooth the inner portion of the helix.

Smoothing the Concha and Triangular Fossa

1. Smooth the concha, as shown here.

2. Also, smooth the triangular fossa.

3. The ridge representing the antihelix and its crura may be smoothed at this time.

Completing the Helix

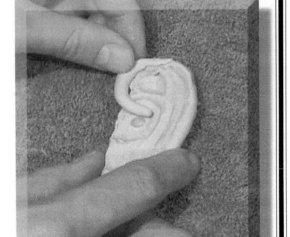

1. To complete the helix, add a small roll of wax to the anterior and superior portion of the ear.

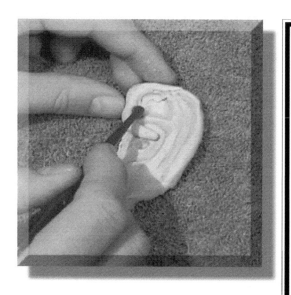

2. With a modeling instrument, attach the roll of wax to the inside of the ear.

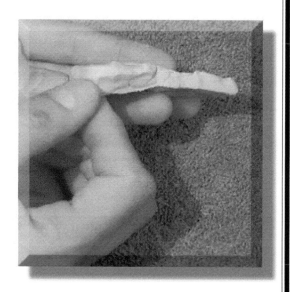

3. Also, attach the roll to the top and backside of the ear.

4. Attach each side of the helix to the floor of the concha.

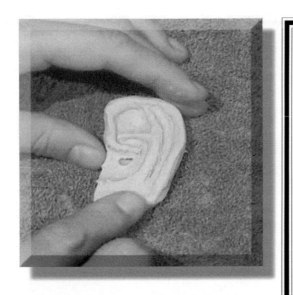

Shaping the Lobe of the Ear

1. If necessary, add wax to the lobe of the ear.

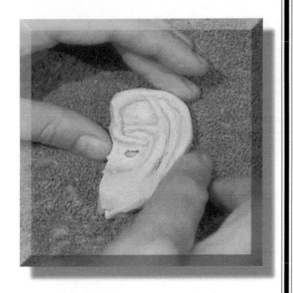

2. Blend this wax into the surrounding adjacent areas.

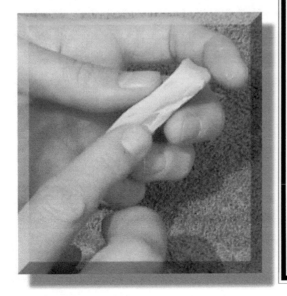

3. Inspect the side and back of the ear. Smooth the wax in these areas.

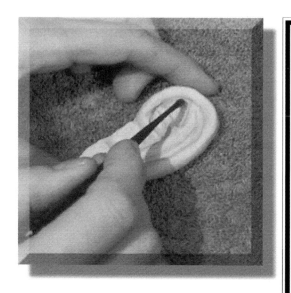

Adding the Inner Depression to the Helix

1. On some subjects, the inner rim of the helix is depressed.
   If necessary, create the depression with a small round end modeling tool.

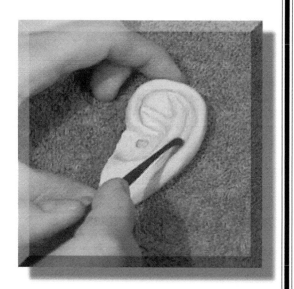

2. Do the same (as #1 above) where the scapha joins the helix.

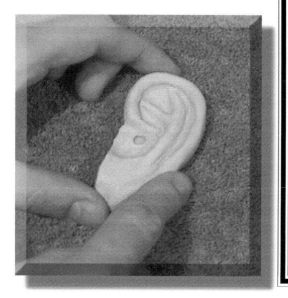

3. Smooth all areas of the ear.

93

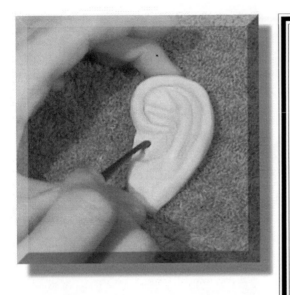

4. Again, check the location of the auditory meatus.
   If necessary, relocate it to its proper position (along the anterior margin of the ear).

Creating the Tragus

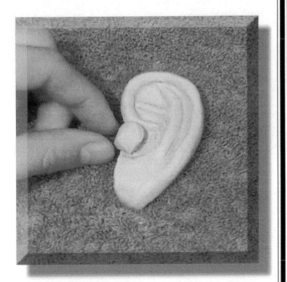

1. To create the tragus, add a pellet of wax along the anterior margin of the ear.

   The tragus covers, but does **not** fill the auditory meatus.

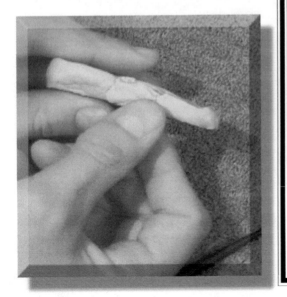

2. Connect the tragus to the anterior margin of the ear.

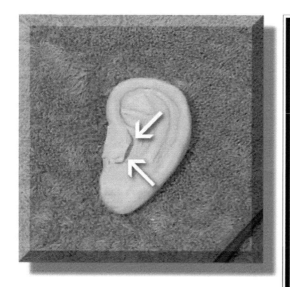

3. Form the proper shape along the posterior margin of the tragus.

Creating the Antitragus and the Intertragic Notch

1. To create the antitragus, add a pellet of wax along the inferior margin of the concha.

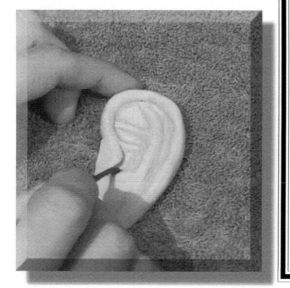

2. To create the intertragic notch, depress the wax found between the tragus and antitragus.
   A small round end modeling tool works well for this task.

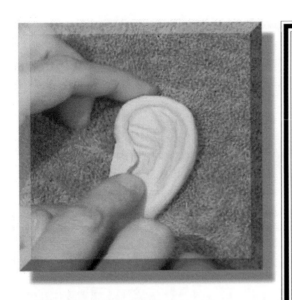

3. Blend the wax into the surrounding structures.

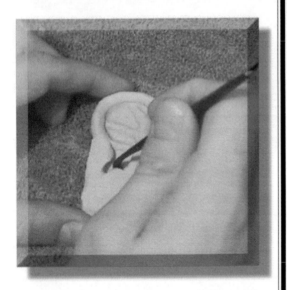

4. With a small modeling tool, connect the antitragus to the inside wall of the concha.

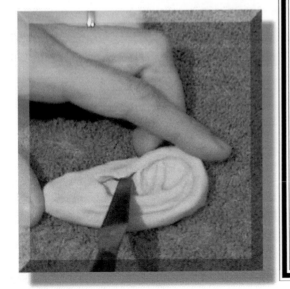

5. Normally, the tragus does not touch the opening of the auditory meatus. If necessary, lift the tragus from the auditory meatus.

6. Smooth the margins of the auditory meatus.

7. Again, smooth all wax areas.

Ear Attachment

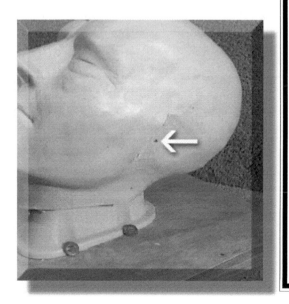

1. Locate the armature's external auditory meatus.

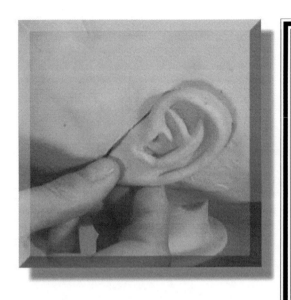

2. Align both ear passages as you place the ear on the side of the head. The anterior margin of the ear rests flush with the lateral cheek.

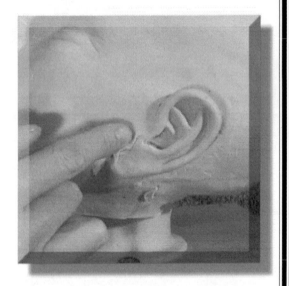

3. Blend the anterior margin of the ear into the lateral cheek.

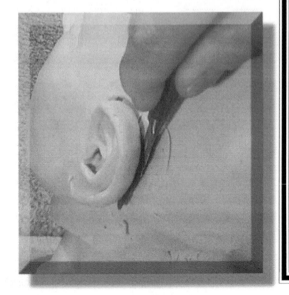

4. Attach the back side of the ear to the head.

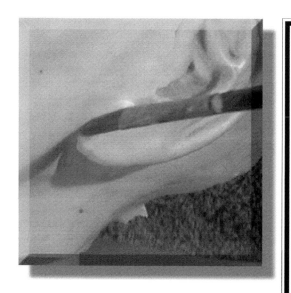

5. If necessary, attach the earlobe to the lateral cheek.
Smooth the area with a solvent saturated brush.

6. Attach the anterior margin of the helix to the lateral cheek. Smooth the wax with a small modeling tool.
Again, a solvent saturated brush will help smooth the area.

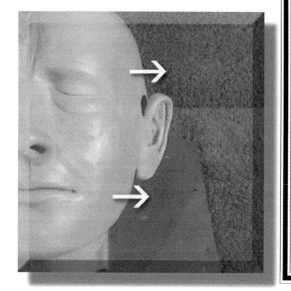

7. Inspect the lateral projection of the ear. If necessary, bend the ear in an outward direction.

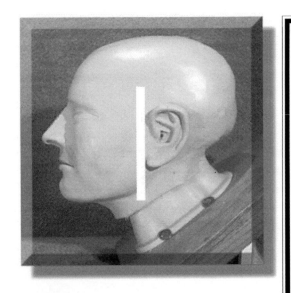

8. Observe the inclination of the anterior margin of the ear.
On some subjects, it may appear vertical
(as shown here).

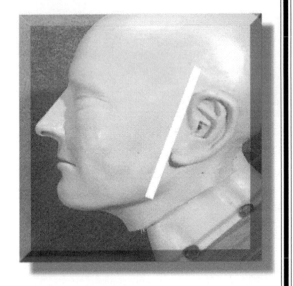

9. On other subjects, the ear may appear inclined.

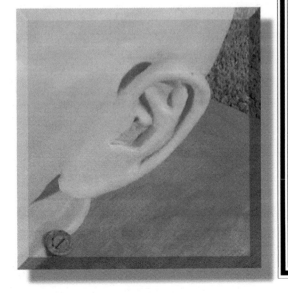

10. Review the form of the ear.

About the Author

A native of South Dakota, Gary Sokoll is an Emeritus Professor in the funeral service department at the University of Central Oklahoma (UCO) in Edmond, Oklahoma. He taught embalming, restorative art, chemistry, and counseling. He is an author, educator, licensed funeral director/embalmer and attorney. He remains active teaching online courses for UCO and St. Petersburg College. In addition, Gary produced educational embalming and restorative art videos. In 2011, Gary retired from his full-time work at UCO, and returned to South Dakota. Gary was instrumental in the evolution of the funeral service department at UCO, and is credited with restoring educational excellence to the program. In his final year he was named national "Educator of the Year" by the American Board of Funeral Service Education (ABFSE), a fitting tribute to a man that has been so influential in the field of funeral service education.

Gary received his bachelor's degree from the University of Central Oklahoma (then known as Central State University), majoring in funeral service. He attended graduate school at South Dakota State University majoring in counseling and guidance and received his M.Ed. Gary went on to attend the University of South Dakota law school, graduating with a Juris Doctor degree. He became a prosecutor for the Office of the State's Attorney in Rapid City, South Dakota before returning to Oklahoma and his association with U.C.O.

Gary and his wife, Pam, reside in Rapid City, South Dakota.